Brown Girl

Written by
Daphnie Glenn

Illustrated by
Shawnna Williams

Palmetto Publishing Group
www.PalmettoPublishingGroup.com

Brown Girl
Copyright ©2018 Daphnie Glenn
www.DaphnieGlenn.com
Illustrated by Shawnna Williams

ISBN-13: 978-1-64111-109-6
ISBN-10: 1-64111-109-7

Brown Girl is dedicated to every girl who has struggled with
self esteem. You were born with a great purpose. Be you and be bold!

I would like to extend a very big thank you to all donors,
including anonymous donors, who made this dream come true!

<u>Gold Package Sponsors</u>
Qwontajah Myers, Mercedes Glenn, Dean Bailey,
and Alanda Posey of Soulful Beginnings, LLC.

Thank you all for starting the conversation!

Makenzie Wilson is a classy brown girl.
With big black hair that her fingers often twirl.

She is beautiful and has all of the brains.

But before she believed it, she would often complain.

My nose is too big and I feel that I am too small!

If only I could grow a few inches and be really tall.

Every night Makenzie would stand in the big mirror to look.
She was not happy with what she saw and her head just shook.

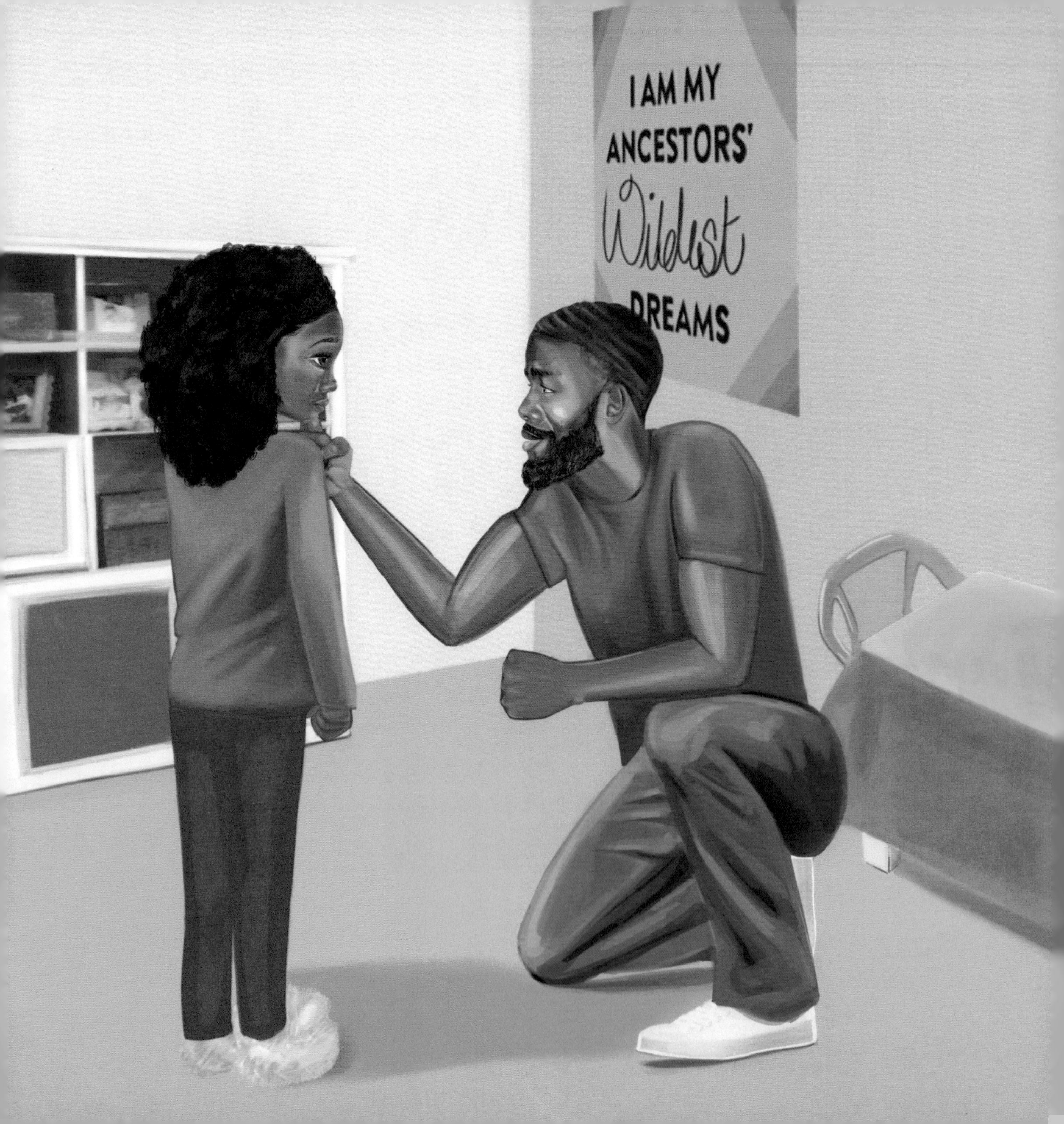
I AM MY
ANCESTORS'
Wildest
DREAMS

Daddy came in just as she prepared herself for bed.

He offered her words of advice and this is what he said.

My *sweet* and precious girl, you are far from plain.

You come from a history of strong women—

so much wisdom to gain!

Their skin much like yours is also magical and brown.

And on top of their big black hair sits a marvelous crown.

As a young girl, they too were upset about

things that seemed unfair.

But they never forgot about the crown

that they needed to wear.

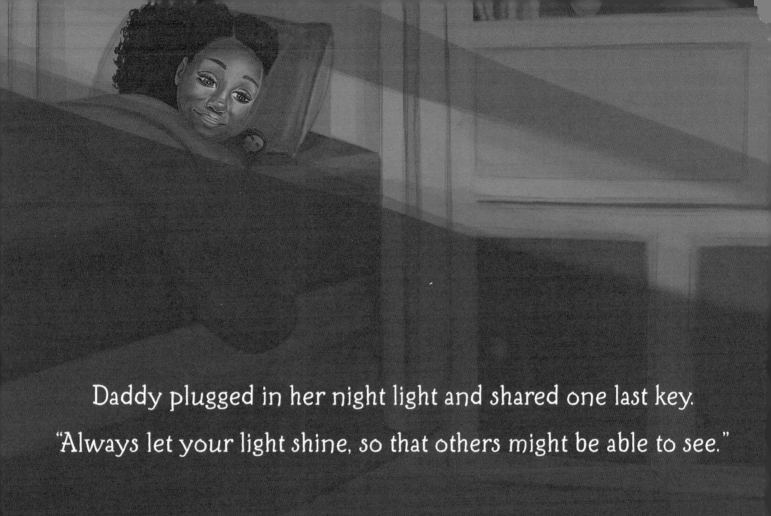

Daddy plugged in her night light and shared one last key.

"Always let your light shine, so that others might be able to see."

...See your good works and special things that you will do.

They were also created for a special purpose- just like you!

Makenzie smiled as her daddy walked to the bedroom door.

She fell into a deep sleep and a dream she would soon explore.

She dreamed about courageous black queens with hearts of steel.

They were brave and bold—something she wished she could feel.

She met Michelle, Maya, and Oprah to name a few! They cheered her on and said, "go brown girl, you can do it too!"

She hugged them all and felt glad that she had someone to relate. Being unhappy in her skin was absolutely not up for debate.

The next morning, she ran to tell her daddy the amazing dream.

"I met Michelle Obama—She was rooting for me and my team!"

Yes brown girl, you can do and be whatever you choose!

You were made perfect—from your head right down to your shoes!

As your daddy, I give you permission to shine.

Set your standards high and let no one alter your Father's design.

Because one day the world will need what you have to offer okay?

Embrace this life! Walk into your purpose each and every day.

Life will never care about what clothes or car you decide.

What will matter most is the love you have for yourself on the inside.

About the Author

♔

Daphnie Glenn of Greenville, SC is the mastermind and youth advocate behind The #StartTheConversation Book Series. Released in 2016, Glenn was called to create books to help children digest the unfortunate events affecting the African American community, in hopes to #StartTheConversation within homes and classrooms. *Brown Boy* has reached the hands of hundreds of children all across the US and holds a top spot for Multicultural Books for Children on Amazon!

Glenn who holds her Master's of Education in Higher Education Administration from Columbia College has always had a commitment to academic excellence, despite her financial disparities growing up. Currently, she serves as an Assistant Director of Housing and Residential Life at her alma mater, University of South Carolina Upstate and is in her third year of teaching. She also serves on Alumni Board of Directors and a Family Fund Committee Member at the university. In her spare time, she loves to read, write, and create memories with her friends and family. She has received many awards including the Talented Tenth Top 10 Young Professionals award sponsored by The Talented Tenth Conference and the South Carolina Black Pages Top 20 under 40 award. To date, she has visited a plethora of schools and organizations throughout the country encouraging the youth and other advocates to begin talking about tough topics. As she continues to create content empowering and educating brown children, she looks forward to sharing books like *Brown Girl* with readers like you!

For speaking engagements, please visit www.DaphnieGlenn.com

About the Illustrator

Portrait Artist and Children's Book Illustrator, Shawnna L. Williams passionately brings book authors' visions to life and creates lifelong mementos for friends and families with custom Oil painted and Pencil-drawn portraits.

Prior to illustrating *Brown Girl*, her most recent book illustrations include, *Brown Boy*, 2017 by Daphnie Glenn, *Aaron Goes to the Police Station*, 2016 (Cover), by Nahjee Grant, and *My Two Dads*, 2016, by Alphonso Buie.

When she's not illustrating books, or creating artwork for national and international clientele, Shawnna's personal works are inspired by resilient, misrepresented and underrepresented groups of people in art and media. She aims to inspire viewers from all walks of life to relate to our common humanity and celebrate our diverse uniqueness.

Her most recent solo exhibition, *"Scars and the Healing Process: from the Individual to the Collective"* was in November 2017 at the Urban Art Gallery in Philadelphia, PA.

Connect with her and view her work on her website, Instagram @drawn2paint, or email at slwportraits@gmail.com.

Made in the USA
Columbia, SC
02 June 2018